Hammer your Grammar

Workbook Grade 1

OM KIDZ
An imprint of Om Books International

WHERE IS IT?

Look at the objects below. Where are they placed? Read the sentences and write the correct answer from the help box.

outside   over   on   in   inside   under

The fish is __________ the bowl.

The parrot is __________ the branch.

The ball is __________ the fence.

The cat is __________ the table.

The lion is __________ the den.

The tree is __________ the house.

MY OR MINE

Read the sentences below. Fill in the blanks with 'my' or 'mine'.

This is __________ book.
This book is __________.

That is __________ ball.
That ball is __________.

This is __________ bag.
This bag is __________.

That is __________ gift.
That gift is __________.

This is __________ hat.
This hat is __________.

That is __________ car.
That car is __________.

NOUNS AROUND

Look at the two children walking in the forest. What do they see around them? Circle the correct nouns from the pebbles below.

boy   girl   elephant   bird

swim   jump   tree   hut

running   eating

WHERE ARE WE?

Where are our animal friends? Fill in the blanks with the correct prepositions to find out.

behind in on inside above

The monkey is sitting __________ the tree.

The bird is flying __________ the forest.

The elephant is walking __________ the stream.

The lion is sitting __________ his den.

The rabbit is hiding __________ the bush.

JUNGLE JUMBLE

What are the animals doing? Guess their actions. Then, find and circle the action words in the grid below.

flying jumping hopping swimming running sleeping

s	l	e	e	p	i	n	g
w	q	a	j	t	f	r	u
i	w	k	u	m	l	u	m
m	e	p	m	s	y	n	p
m	h	o	p	p	i	n	g
i	a	l	i	m	n	i	h
n	z	k	n	m	g	n	o
g	p	u	g	i	z	g	l

MERRY ME

This little boy is introducing his animal friends to us. Can you circle the adjectives in his introductions?

This huge elephant loves to swim.

This naughty monkey loves to trick everyone.

This fierce lion is the king of the jungle.

This funny bunny likes to joke around.

This scary alligator stays in the lake all day long.

This cute bear smiles all the time.

PRONOUN PATHS

Help Polly the Parrot learn his pronouns by filling the blanks with the correct words.

it they he she they

My parrot likes to sing. ______________ sings beautifully.

My brother went to the jungle. ______________ saw many animals there.

My mother has a pet dog. ______________ named him Dodo.

Wild animals live in the jungle. ______________ also live in zoos.

The lion and the tiger are sleeping. ______________ are tired.

RIGHT ROCK

Choose the correct word on the rock to complete the sentences below.

The (son / sun) is shining through the trees.

Look at the lion's (paws / pause)!

The jungle has many (rows / rose) of trees.

The (two / to) deer are running.

(Where / Wear) is little Toto going?

LEAFY FILLERS

Fill in the leaves with the correct articles to complete the sentences.

Is this ________________ bird's nest?

There is ________________ apple under that tree.

I can see ________________ tree with orange leaves.

The hen has laid ________________ egg.

________________ elephant is walking towards us.

SYNONYM SORTING

Read the words and cross out the flower whose word doesn't share its meaning with the others.

jungle	woods	forest	form
animal	beast	flower	wildlife
sing	hum	chirp	yell
crawl	creep	jump	slither
sleep	climb	ascend	scale

OPPOSITE PAIRS

Look at the animals and fill in the blanks with the correct opposites.

short **cold** **small** **slow** **young** **awake**

The elephant is **big** but the ant is _______.

The giraffe is **tall** and the rabbit is _______.

The forest is **hot** but the mountains are _______.

The hare is **fast** but the tortoise is _______.

The lion is **asleep** in his den but the tiger is _______.

This horse is **old** but the foal is _______.

ANIMAL TALK

Animals can talk too! Can you match these animals to the sounds they make?

- bleat
- quack
- chirp
- croak
- cackle
- hoot
- neigh
- moo
- roar
- trumpet
- hiss
- bray

JUNIOR JUMBLE

What are these animal babies called? Rearrange the letters to know their names.

b u c

e y o j

l a f c

m a l b

g n i l k c u d

BIRTHDAY GROUPS

Larry the Lion is inviting animal groups for his birthday. Fill in the correct collective nouns to help him know who is attending.

A ____________ of elephants.

A ____________ of bees.

An ____________ of frogs.

A ____________ of monkeys.

An ____________ of tigers.

ONE OR MANY

Look at all these jungle animals. Can you write their plurals in the boxes given alongside?

PARTY PAIRS

These animals are attending the lion's party in pairs. Can you fill in the blanks with the correct gender?

rooster and ______

______ and cow

horse and ______

______ and duck

tiger and ______

ANIMAL RHYME

Chichi the Cat went to the jungle and wrote a poem about the animals she saw. Can you circle the rhyming words in them?

I went to the jungle and met a monkey
He swung around a lot and acted very funky.

Then I met a big brown bear
Who looked very big and had lots of hair.

I saw a lion in his den
His roar was louder than 20 men.

The elephant with a trunk for his nose
Was sweet enough to give me a rose.

The jungle is such a fun place to be
Let's go back there, you and me.

ALL ABOUT ME

Terry the Tiger wants to give a speech. Fill in the blanks with 'I', 'me', 'my', 'mine' and 'myself' to complete his speech.

Good morning, jungle folks. __________ would like to talk to all of you today.
Are you listening to __________? Let's begin!
__________ friend, the cheetah, needs your help. Any friend of __________ is a friend to all of you. And we must help our friends.
A strange cheetah from another forest stole his den last night. I tried to help him __________ but the new cheetah is mean. He fought with __________ and __________ friend. I cannot fight this new animal __________. Can you help __________ and __________ friend teach this naughty cheetah a lesson?

Thank you!

A VISIT TO THE JUNGLE

Binky and Jojo went to the jungle. Can you complete their sentences by choosing the correct word?

Is (that/those) a cat I see behind the trees?

(This/These) bear is so furry!

Are (that/those) monkeys hanging from the tree?

(This/These) croaking sounds are made by (that/these) frog.

(That/Those) flowers smell wonderful, don't they?

(This/Those) lions look scary!

Let's stay closer to (this/these) bear.

Look at (that/these) bird flying in the sky!

(This/These) elephant is swimming in the pond.

Let's say hello to (those/that) hippos before we go home.

CONNECTING PATHS

Match the columns correctly to form sentences.

There are many wild animals	but	no one can spot it easily.
A chameleon changes colour	and	we didn't have any bread.
We wanted to feed the ducks	or	go to the jungle?
Should we visit the zoo	so	birds in the jungle.

JUNGLE CROSSWORD

Solve the riddles and complete the jungle crossword.

I am the king of the jungle. 

I stay awake at night. 

I am the largest animal on land. 

I can talk just like you. 

I am the ship of the desert. 

I have spots and I can run. 

l	r	o	g	l	r	o	g	k	l	m	n	q
l	w	x	t	i	w	e	t	u	r	t	l	s
i	o	q	e	o	w	l	o	o	o	i	s	u
z	a	p	a	n	a	e	a	a	s	n	a	i
e	g	f	o	g	g	p	a	r	r	o	t	k
b	o	h	y	h	x	h	h	h	e	l	e	j
i	r	s	r	a	c	a	m	e	l	i	s	u
z	b	a	c	d	b	n	c	d	e	n	a	i
e	f	g	h	p	f	t	h	p	o	a	c	k
b	c	h	a	m	c	h	a	m	p	l	e	j
r	s	r	p	a	s	r	p	a	a	r	o	k
a	t	q	p	o	t	q	p	o	r	i	z	d
l	u	o	s	t	u	o	s	t	d	i	c	n

ANIMAL ORDER

Let's rearrange these animals by writing their names in alphabetical order.

fox

lion

deer

giraffe

elephant

zebra

rhino

hippo

ANIMAL BUILDER

Look at the picture clues and combine their names to make new words.

 +  =

 +  =

 +  =

 +  =

 +  =

STORY TIME

Baby hippo wants to tell her friends a lovely story, but she got the order wrong! Number these sentences in the correct order to form a story.

A thirsty crow was flying in search of water. ☐

The water began to rise and the crow could drink it. ☐

So, he had an idea. ☐

He found a pitcher of water. ☐

He began to drop pebbles into the water. ☐

He drank the water and flew away happily. ☐

But, his beak could not reach the water. ☐

PROVERB PUZZLE

Match the proverbs to their meanings.

Proverb	Meaning
Birds of a feather flock together.	It's raining heavily.
Don't put the cart before the horse.	Don't dream of things before they happen.
If wishes were horses, then beggars would ride.	Do not reverse the correct order.
It's raining cats and dogs.	Wishing for something is not the same as getting it.
Don't count your chickens before they hatch.	Similar people will stick together.

STORY TIME

Read the story and tick the correct answers for the questions.

Once upon a time, there lived a lion. He was the king of the jungle. He lived in a big den. One day, he called all the animals for his birthday party. But the animals were scared. They thought the lion wanted to gobble them up. So no one wanted to go to the party. The lion felt sad. He went to the animals and said, "I don't want to gobble you up. I want to be your friend!" The animals felt sorry for him. They went for his party. And they had so much fun! The lion was a nice animal after all.

Who was the king of the jungle?

a. Lion b. Tiger

What did he invite the animals for?

a. Dinner party b. Birthday party

What did the lion want to do?

a. Gobble the animals b. Be their friend

Who felt sorry for the lion?

a. No one b. The animals

Who was a nice animal in the end?

a. The lion b. The rabbit

PICTURE TALK

Look at the picture and write a small story about it.

ANSWERS

Page 2

The fish is **in** the bowl.

The ball is **over** the fence.

The lion is **inside** the den.

The parrot is **on** the branch.

The cat is **under** the table.

The tree is **outside** the house.

Page 3

This is **my** book.
This book is **mine**.

That is **my** ball.
That ball is **mine**.

This is **my** bag.
This bag is **mine**.

That is **my** gift.
That gift is **mine**.

This is **my** hat.
This hat is **mine**.

That is **my** car.
That car is **mine**.

Page 4

boy (circled), girl (circled), elephant, bird (circled)
swim, jump, tree (circled), hut (circled)
running, eating

Page 5

The monkey is sitting **on** the tree.

The bird is flying **above** the forest.

The elephant is walking **in** the stream.

The lion is sitting **inside** his den.

The rabbit is hiding **behind** the bush.

Page 6

s	l	e	e	p	i	n	g
w	q	a	j	t	f	r	u
i	w	k	u	m	l	u	m
m	e	p	m	s	y	n	p
m	h	o	p	p	i	n	g
i	a	l	i	m	n	i	h
n	z	k	n	m	g	n	o
g	p	u	g	i	z	g	l

Page 7

This (huge) elephant loves to swim.

This (naughty) monkey loves to trick everyone.

This (fierce) lion is the king of the jungle.

This (funny) bunny likes to joke around.

This (scary) alligator stays in the lake all day long.

This (cute) bear smiles all the time.

Page 8

My parrot likes to sing. **It** sings beautifully.

My brother went to the jungle. **He** saw many animals there.

My mother has a pet dog. **She** named him Dodo.

Wild animals live in the jungle. **They** also live in zoos.

The lion and the tiger are sleeping. **They** are tired.

Page 9

The (son / **sun**) is shining through the trees.

Look at the lion's (**paws** / pause)!

The jungle has many (**rows** / rose) of trees.

The (**two** / to) deer are running.

(**Where** / Wear) is little Toto going?

Page 10

Is this **a** bird's nest?

There is **an** apple under that tree.

I can see **a** tree with orange leaves.

The hen has laid **an** egg.

An elephant is walking towards us.

Page 11

jungle, woods, forest, ~~form~~

animal, beast, ~~flower~~, wildlife

sing, hum, chirp, ~~yell~~

crawl, creep, ~~jump~~, slither

~~sleep~~, climb, ascend, scale

Page 12

The elephant is big but the ant is **small**.

The giraffe is tall and the rabbit is **short**.

The forest is hot but the mountains are **cold**.

The hare is fast but the tortoise is **slow**.

The lion is asleep in his den but the tiger is **awake**.

This horse is old but the foal is **young**.

Page 13

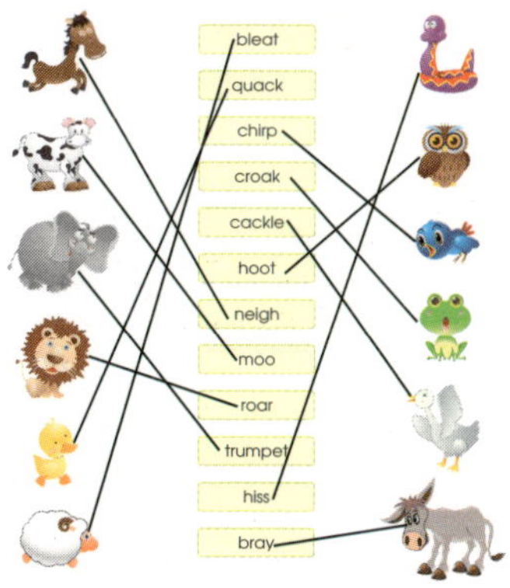

Page 14

buc	cub
eyoj	joey
lafc	calf
malb	lamb
gnilkcud	duckling

Page 15

A **herd** of elephants.

A **swarm** of bees.

An **army** of frogs.

A **troop** of monkeys.

An **ambush** of tigers.

Page 16

geese

oxen

deer

sheep

mice

ducks

Page 17

rooster and **hen**

bull and cow

horse and **mare**

drake and duck

tiger and **tigress**

ANSWERS

Page 18

I went to the jungle and met a monkey.
He swung around a lot and acted
very funky.
Then I met a big brown bear
Who looked very big and had lots of hair.
I saw a lion sleeping in his den
His snoring was louder than 20 men.
The elephant with a trunk for his nose
Was sweet enough to give me a rose.
The jungle is such a fun place to be
Let's go back there, you and me.

Page 19

Good morning, jungle folk. **I** would like to talk to all of you today.
Are you listening to **me**? Let's begin! **My** friend, the cheetah, needs your help.
Any friend of **mine** is a friend to all of you.
And we must help our friends.
A strange cheetah from another forest stole his den last night. I tried to help him **myself** but the new cheetah is mean. He fought with **me** and **my** friend. I cannot fight this new animal **myself**. Can you help **me** and **my** friend to teach this naughty cheetah a lesson?

Thank you!

Pages 20-21

Is **that** a cat I see behind the trees?

This bear is so furry!

Are **those** monkeys hanging from the tree?

These croaking sounds are made by that frog.

Those flowers smell wonderful, don't they?

Those lions look scary!

Let's stay closer to **this** bear.

Look at **that** bird flying in the sky!

This elephant is swimming in the pond.

Let's say hello to **those** hippos before we go home.

Page 22

There are many wild animals **and** birds in the jungle.
A chameleon changes colour **so** no one can spot it easily.
We wanted to feed the ducks **but** we didn't have any bread.
Should we visit the zoo **or** go to the jungle?

Page 23

Page 24

Page 25

grasshopper

honeybee

horseback

ladybird

starfish

Page 26

A thirsty crow was flying in search of water.
He found a pitcher of water.
But, his beak could not reach the water.
So, he had an idea.
He began to drop pebbles into the water.
The water began to rise and the crow could drink it.
He drank the water and flew away happily.

Page 27

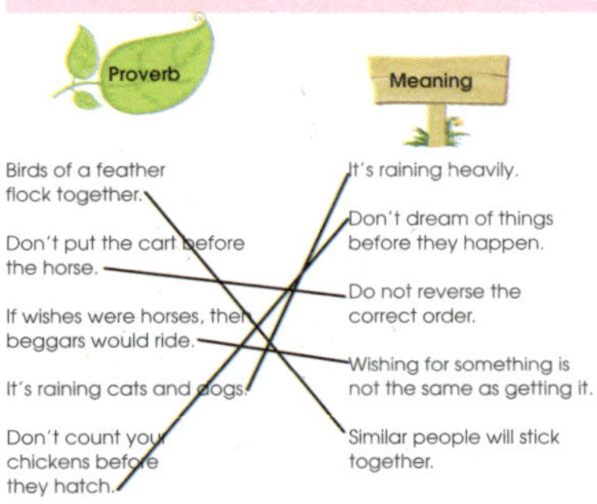

Pages 28-29

Who was the king of the jungle?

a. **Lion** b. Tiger

What did he invite the animals for?

a. Dinner party b. **Birthday party**

What did the lion want to do?

a. Gobble the animals b. **Be their friend**

Who felt sorry for the lion?

a. No one b. **The animals**

Who was a nice animal in the end?

a. **The lion** b. The rabbit

Hammer your Grammar

Workbook Grade 2

OM KIDZ

An imprint of Om Books International

SENTENCE SCRAMBLE

Happy the Hippo has messed up his sentences! Tick the ones that make sense and cross out the ones that don't.

Cuckoos sweet sing. ☐

Mary has a little lamb. ☐

I going to are the zoo. ☐

I will feed my cat. ☐

My animal favourite are dog. ☐

Camels are usually found in deserts. ☐

Is the monkey eating a banana? ☐

NAME SORTING

Help Tickles the Tiger sort out the nouns from these sentences in the correct column.

A herd of cattle is passing by.

Mojo the monkey is looking at me.

Elephants are the largest animals on land.

We named our dog Lucy.

The Gir forest has lions.

Have you seen that litter of kittens?

The hyena's laughter was scary.

Proper	Common	Abstract	Collective

ONCE UPON A NOUN

Help Bingo the Bear underline the countable nouns in **BLUE** and the uncountable nouns in **RED**.

Once upon a time, there lived a family of three bears in the woods. They were Mama Bear, Papa Bear and Baby Bear. One day, they went out for a walk. Mama Bear cooked up some delicious porridge before they left.

While they were gone, a little girl named Goldilocks walked by their house. She smelt the porridge and her tummy began to rumble. She went in and saw three bowls on the table.

She ran towards them and took a spoonful of Papa Bear's porridge. But it was too hot. Then, she grabbed a spoonful of Mama Bear's porridge. But it was too cold. Finally, she tried Baby Bear's porridge. It was just right! She ate it all up hungrily.

After a while, she felt sleepy. She spotted Papa Bear's bed, but it was too hard. She lay down on Mama Bear's bed, but it was too soft. Finally, she tried Baby Bear's bed, which was just right. She jumped onto the bed and fell asleep in a jiffy!

Soon, the bears returned home. Baby Bear started crying when he saw his porridge bowl empty. "Somebody ate all my porridge!" he cried and ran to his room. And what did he see there? A strange little girl fast asleep on his bed! Baby bear screamed loudly. Goldilocks woke up. She was shocked to see three angry bears at the foot of the bed. She jumped out and ran away as fast as she could.

SENTENCE SORTER

Let's help Laurie the Lion circle the subjects and underline the predicates in the sentences below.

Singing birds make us happy.

A camel is called the ship of the desert.

Forests have a variety of trees.

Cows give us milk.

Wild animals live in jungles.

Dogs are a man's best friend.

SOUND ALOUD

Help Hagrid the Hippo choose the correct homophones to complete the sentence.

A horse is ______, whereas a mare is female.

a. mail b. male

There are ______ many bees in this forest.

a. too b. two

We saw a ______ on our hiking trip.

a. deer b. dear

Did you ______ the sound of the bear?

a. here b. hear

The cat is ______ favourite pet.

a. their b. there

The ______ lost the race.

a. hair b. hare

ARTICLE TRACKER

Leo the Leopard wrote a poem but forgot to add articles. Can you add articles in the correct places?

Once there was ________ cute little leopard,
But he didn't want to be cute,
He wanted to be ________ shepherd!

What he loved most was to keep
________ close, watchful eye
On those naughty little sheep.

He liked to watch them graze all day
Then lead them back home
For ________ good night's stay.

But the sheep didn't like
________ leopard too much
They were afraid of his sharp touch.

When they saw ________ leopard coming by
They ran as fast
As their little feet could try.

________ leopard was sad, but what could he do
He gave up being ________ shepherd
And went to ________ zoo!

VERBIE WORM

Verbie the Worm wants you to circle all the verbs in these sentences and connect them to his basket.

The hungry lion is roaring.

The owl is hiding because it is daytime.

The crow is flying down to steal the cheese.

Goldilocks fell asleep on baby bear's bed.

The animals are drinking water from the stream.

Why is your dog walking like that?

She took her cat to the vet.

All his friends thanked the bear.

The crafty fox hides behind that bush every day.

A tiny mouse lived under the hole.

TIGER TENSE

Help Timmy the Tiger name the tenses of the underlined words. Write whether they are present, past or future tense on the blanks below.

The bird is flying high up in the sky.

____

I will take my dog for a walk shortly.

____

The boy saw how the elephant was being bathed.

____

The cat rolled in the sand and got dirty.

____

My pet dog is drinking milk this morning.

____

ADJECTIVE HUNT

Ronnie the Rhino is on an adjective quest. Spot and circle all the adjectives in the grid.

s	l	e	b	s	l	e	p	o	n	g
w	q	f	e	r	o	c	t	g	r	u
i	w	b	a	i	w	k	m	r	u	m
m	f	e	r	o	c	i	o	u	s	p
g	r	a	c	e	f	u	l	m	c	g
i	w	u	i	i	w	k	m	p	a	m
m	e	t	p	r	e	t	t	y	r	p
m	h	i	u	m	s	l	i	m	y	g
i	w	f	l	d	h	i	l	a	z	y
n	z	u	n	n	y	k	n	z	a	n
s	h	l	g	g	p	u	w	i	l	d

QUALITY OR QUANTITY?

Read the sentences and help Jenny the Giraffe decide whether they have adjectives of quality or quantity.

The dog has two puppies. ____________

The giraffe is a tall animal. ____________

The crafty fox wanted the cheese. ____________

Some birds cannot fly. ____________

There are many species of animals, birds and insects to be found. ____________

Elephants have long trunks. ____________

Dinosaurs are extinct animals. ____________

ARNIE'S ADVERBS

Arnie the Ant wants to fill up the jungle with adverbs. Help him add the correct ones to these sentences first!

Hyenas laugh ________________.

A cat can catch a mouse ________________.

Cheetahs run ________________.

We ________________ go trekking in the forest.

The little bird sang ________________.

GENDER BENDER

Builder the Beaver is constructing a gender chart. Can you help him fill in the correct words?

If a cow is female, a male is a __________.

If a tigress is female, a male is a __________.

If a lioness is female, a male is a __________.

If a sow is a female panda, a male is a __________.

If a hen is female, a male is a __________.

COUNT AND MATCH

Match these singular animals to their plural forms.

macaw	squirrels
squirrel	rhinoceroses
rhinoceros	mongooses
mongoose	macaws

WORD WHIZ

Help Oliver the Owl understand synonyms and antonyms. Read the sentences. Mark the synonyms with 'S' and the antonyms with 'A' in the boxes alongside.

This is a dense forest.	crammed	☐	clear	☐
Wild beasts inhabit the forest.	mild	☐	untamed	☐
Pretty flowers grow amidst the trees.	beautiful	☐	repulsive	☐
Our ecology needs to be preserved.	destroyed	☐	conserved	☐
The berries that grow here are delicious.	nasty	☐	tasty	☐
A clear stream is flowing here.	murky	☐	clean	☐
The antelope has big horns.	small	☐	large	☐

PICKING PRONOUNS

Polly the Parrot needs to pick out the correct pronouns to complete these sentences. Can you help him?

(I / She) like animals.

Jack and (I / me) are watching a movie about bears.

(That / These) puppy needs water.

Dolly likes turtles. (She / He) has got one as a pet.

Mary told (me / I) an interesting story about elephants.

LEAFY LINKS

Choose the correct word from the flowers to complete the sentences below.

There are clouds ______ the sky.

The sun is shining from ______ the clouds.

The giraffe is walking ______ the elephant.

Can you see that bird ______ the two trees?

The crocodile is swimming ______ the river.

We can see fish swimming ______ the water.

The woodpecker vanished ______ its nest.

Flowers are growing ______ those trees.

The monkey is swinging ______ tree to tree.

The shepherd is sitting ______ his sheep.

in | from | behind | near

under | beside | between | across

COME TOGETHER

Join and rewrite the following sentences using a preposition from the flowers.

as | so | even | because

though | since | when | while

The fox wanted the cheese. He flattered the crow.

____

The turtle didn't give up. He was slow.

____

No one came to help the shepherd. He had cried wolf many times.

____

____

The ant did not help the grasshopper. He was lazy.

____

The stork ate her dinner. The fox watched.

____

ERROR SPOTTER

Spot and circle the errors in the sentences below.

Where I can find a pet shop?

We have visited Ranthambore sanctuary last weekend.

The woman which works as forest officer is from my city.

Although it was raining but we had the hike.

I look forward to meet my friends outside the woods.

Every animals likes freedom.

EXCLAIM THAT!

Spot and circle the interjections from the pebbles below.

Ouch

Water

Phew

Book

Hey

Yikes

Oh no

Grammar

Wow

Coffee

Turtle

Soup

PROVERB PROBLEMS

Mojo the Monkey messed up all these proverbs! Rearrange the words in the correct order to make meaningful proverbs.

change leopard spots cannot A its

____

silk monkey monkey less no A is a in

____

rotten barrel A spoils apple the

____

An snared old easily fox not is

____

paints A picture words thousand a

____

The worm the early catches bird

____

can lead can't a drink horse to,
you make You but water him

____

____

INSPECTOR IDIOM

Help Inspector Eagle spot and circle the idioms in these sentences.

Please be clear, do not beat around the bush.

Trying to learn karate like this is not right,
you are barking up the wrong tree.

Let someone else hear that cock and bull story.

Cry wolf, and you are sure to learn your lesson.

The first ranker turned out to be a dark horse.

Don't count your chickens before they hatch.

Hold your horses, hard work always pays.

SPELLCHECK

Help these animals spell their names correctly by filling the blanks with the correct letters.

Rhino __ __ ros

Hippopo __ __ mus

T __ __ can

M __ __ aw

R __ __ ndeer

PUNCTUATION PROBLEMS

Help Rory the Reindeer rewrite these sentences with the correct punctuation marks.

where is the dogs kennel

____

jills dog is barking

____

Wow I like your goldfish.

____

I saw elephants giraffes zebras and bears at the zoo

____

____

oh I love this book about different forests

____

____

ALL ABOUT ANIMALS

Read the paragraph below and answer the questions on the next page.

The jungle stretches over vast expanses. For miles and miles, all you see is a stretch of land. Wait! A quick streak seems to be moving through this wide, empty space. If you look closely, you can see a spotted blur running at an unbelievable speed. It is the cheetah, the fastest animal on land.

Cheetahs have long, slender bodies that help them move at a quick pace. They use their tails to steer in the right direction.

These amazing animals belong to the cat family, just like lions and tigers. However, unlike their cousins, cheetahs do not let out loud, scary roars. They purr, just like your friendly little house cat!

Cheetahs hunt mostly during the day, either late in the morning or early in the evening. They chase their prey and pounce on them in a matter of seconds, gobbling up their meals instantly.

Who is the fastest animal on land?

____

Which family does the cheetah belong to?

____

What sound does a cheetah make?

____

When do cheetahs hunt?

____

How do cheetahs move in different directions while running?

____

DEAR ANIMALS

Bobby wants to write a letter to all the animals he visited when he went to the jungle. Can you help him write the letter?

To,

From,

FABULOUS FABLES

Look at the picture, read the lines below and complete the rest of the story.

Once upon a time, there lived a lazy shepherd boy. He didn't look after his sheep too well. Everyday, he took his sheep up the hill and left them alone while he napped under a tree. One day, ______________________________

____

____

____

____

____

____

____

JUNGLE QUEST

Let's write a story about the jungle. Look at these animals and write a story about them.

ANSWERS

Page 2

Cuckoos sweet sing. ✗

Mary has a little lamb. ✓

I going to are the zoo. ✗

I will feed my cat. ✓

My animal favourite are dog. ✗

Camels are usually found in deserts. ✓

Is the monkey eating a banana? ✓

Page 3

A herd of cattle is passing by.
Mojo the monkey is looking at me.
Elephants are the largest animals on land.
We named our dog Lucy.
The Gir forest has lions.
Have you seen that litter of kittens?
The hyena's laughter was scary.

Proper	Common	Abstract	Collective
Mojo	cattle	laughter	herd
Lucy	monkey		litter
Gir	elephants		
	lions		

Pages 4-5

Once upon a time, there lived a family of three bears in the woods. They were Mama Bear, Papa Bear and Baby Bear. One day, they went out for a walk. Mama Bear cooked up some delicious porridge before they left.

While they were gone, a little girl named Goldilocks walked by their house. She smelt the porridge and her tummy began to rumble. She went in and saw three bowls on the table. She ran towards them and took a spoonful of Papa Bear's porridge. But it was too hot. Then, she grabbed a spoonful of Mama Bear's porridge. But it was too cold. Finally, she tried Baby Bear's porridge. It was just right! She ate it all up hungrily.

After a while, she felt sleepy. She spotted Papa Bear's bed, but it was too hard. She lay down on Mama Bear's bed, but it was too soft. Finally, she tried Baby Bear's bed, which was just right. She jumped onto the bed and fell asleep in a jiffy!

Soon, the bears returned home. Baby Bear started crying when he saw his porridge bowl empty. "Somebody ate all my porridge!" he cried and ran to his room. And what did he see there? A strange little girl fast asleep on his bed! Baby bear screamed loudly. Goldilocks woke up. She was shocked to see three angry bears at the foot of the bed. She jumped out and ran away as fast as she could.

Page 6

(Singing birds) make us happy.

(A camel) is called the ship of the desert.

(Forests) have a variety of trees.

(Cows) give us milk.

(Wild animals) live in jungles.

(Dogs) are a man's best friend.

Page 7

A horse is the ______, whereas the mare is the female.
a. mail b. male

There are ______ many bees in this forest.
a. too b. two

We saw a ______ on our hiking trip.
a. deer b. dear

Did you ______ the sound of the bear?
a. here b. hear

The cat is ______ favourite pet.
a. their b. there

The ______ lost the race.
a. hair b. hare

Page 8

Once there was **a** cute little leopard,
But he didn't want to be cute,
He wanted to be **a** shepherd!

What he loved most was to keep
A close, watchful eye
On those naughty little sheep.

He liked to watch them graze all day
Then lead them back home
For **a** good night's stay.

But the sheep didn't like **the** leopard too much
They were afraid of his sharp touch.

When they saw **the** leopard coming by
They ran as fast
As their little feet could try.

The leopard was sad, but what could he do
He gave up being **a** shepherd
And went to **a** zoo!

Page 9

The hungry lion is (roaring).

The owl is (hiding) because it is daytime.

The crow is (flying) down to (steal) the cheese.

Goldilocks (fell asleep) on baby bear's bed.

The animals are (drinking) water from the stream.

Why is your dog (walking) like that?

She (took) her cat to the vet.

All his friends (thanked) the bear.

The crafty fox (hides) behind that bush every day.

A tiny mouse (lived) under the hole.

Page 10

The bird is flying high up in the sky.
present tense

I will take my dog for a walk shortly.
future tense

The boy saw how the elephant was being bathed.
past tense

The cat rolled in the sand and got dirty.
past tense

My pet dog is drinking milk this morning.
present tense

Page 11

s	l	e	b	s	l	e	p	o	n	g
w	q	f	e	r	o	c	t	g	r	u
i	w	b	a	i	w	k	m	r	u	m
m	f	e	r	o	c	i	o	u	s	p
g	r	a	c	e	f	u	l	m	c	g
i	w	u	i	i	w	k	m	p	a	m
m	e	t	p	r	e	t	t	y	r	p
m	h	i	u	m	s	l	i	m	y	g
i	w	f	l	d	h	i	l	a	z	y
n	z	u	n	n	y	k	n	z	a	n
s	h	l	g	g	p	u	w	i	l	d

Page 12

The dog has two puppies.
adjective of quantity

The giraffe is a tall animal.
adjective of quality

The crafty fox wanted the cheese.
adjective of quality

Some birds cannot fly.
adjective of quantity

There are many species of animals, birds and insects to be found.
adjective of quantity

Elephants have long trunks.
adjective of quality

Dinosaurs are extinct animals.
adjective of quality

Page 13

Hyenas laugh **loudly**.

A cat can catch a mouse **easily**.

Cheetahs run **quickly**.

We **often** go trekking in the forest.

The little bird sang **joyfully**.

Page 14

If a cow is female, a male is a **bull**.

If a tigress is female, a male is a **tiger**.

If a lioness is female, a male is a **lion**.

If a sow is a female panda, a male is a **bear**.

If a hen is female, a male is a **rooster**.

Page 15

macaw	squirrels
squirrel	rhinoceroses
rhinoceros	mongooses
mongoose	macaws

Page 16

This is a dense forest.

Wild beasts inhabit the forest.

Pretty flowers grow amidst the trees.

Our ecology needs to be preserved.

The berries that grow here are delicious.

A clear stream is flowing here.

The antelope has big horns.

crammed	S	clear	A
mild	A	untamed	S
beautiful	S	repulsive	A
destroyed	A	conserved	S
nasty	A	tasty	S
murky	A	clean	S
small	A	large	S

Page 17

(**I** / She) like animals.

Jack and (**I** / me) are watching a movie about bears.

(**That** / These) puppy needs water.

Dolly likes turtles. (**She** / He) has got one as a pet.

Mary told (**me** / I) an interesting story about elephants.

ANSWERS

Page 18

There are clouds **in** the sky.

The sun is shining from **behind** the clouds.

The giraffe is walking **beside** the elephant.

Can you see that bird **between** the two trees?

The crocodile is swimming **across** the river.

We can see fish swimming **under** the water.

The woodpecker vanished **near** its nest.

Flowers are growing **near** those trees.

The monkey is swinging **from** tree to tree.

The shepherd is sitting **near** his sheep.

Page 19

The fox wanted the cheese. He flattered the crow.
The fox wanted the cheese **so** he flattered the crow.

The turtle didn't give up. He was slow.
The turtle didn't give up **even though** he was slow.

No one came to help the shepherd. He had cried wolf many times.
No one came to help the shepherd **because** he had cried wolf many times.

The ant did not help the grasshopper. He was lazy.
The ant did not help the grasshopper **because** he was lazy.

The stork ate her dinner. The fox watched.
The stork ate her dinner **while** the fox watched.

Page 20

Where I can find a pet shop?

We have visited Ranthambore sanctuary last weekend.

The woman which works as forest officer is from Maharashtra.

Although it was raining but we had the hike.

I look forward to meet my friends outside the woods.

Every animals likes freedom.

Page 21

Page 22

change leopard spots cannot A its
A leopard cannot change its spots.

silk monkey monkey less no A is a in
A monkey in silk is no less a monkey.

rotten barrel A spoils apple the
A rotten apple spoils the barrel.

An snared old easily fox not is
An old fox is not easily snared.

paints A picture words thousand a
A picture paints a thousand words.

The worm the early catches bird
The early bird catches the worm.

can lead can't a drink horse to, you make You but water him
You can lead a horse to water but you can't make him drink.

Page 23

Please be clear, do not beat around the bush.

Trying to learn karate like this is not right, you are barking up the wrong tree.

Let someone else her that cock and bull story.

Cry wolf, and you are sure to learn your lesson.

The first ranker turned out to be a dark horse.

Don't count your chickens before they hatch.

Hold your horses, hard work always pays.

Page 24

Page 25

where is the dogs kennel
Where is the dog's kennel?

jills dog is barking
Jill's dog is barking.

Wow I like your goldfish.
Wow! I like your goldfish.

I saw elephants giraffes zebras and bears at the zoo
I saw elephants, giraffes, zebras and bears at the zoo.

oh I love this book about different forests
Oh! I love this book about different forests.

Pages 26-27

Answer the questions given below.

Who is the fastest animal on land?
The cheetah.

Which family does the cheetah belong to?
The cat family.

What sound does a cheetah make?
A purring sound.

When do cheetahs hunt?
Mostly during the day, either late in the morning or early in the evening.

How do cheetahs move in different directions while running?
They use their tails to steer in the right direction.

Hammer your Grammar

Workbook Grade 3

OM KIDZ

An imprint of Om Books International

GRAZING FOR WORDS

Read the sentences and circle as directed.

Cows give milk. (Identify the nouns)

They eat grass. (Identify the pronoun)

These cows are white in colour. (Identify the adjective)

They are walking in the meadows. (Identify the verb)

The cows have very cute bells around their necks. (Identify the adverb)

That cow is sitting under a tree. (Identify the preposition)

This cow is white and that one is brown. (Identify the conjunction)

Oh! Their milk is so sweet! (Identify the interjection)

APOSTROPHIC ANTS

Help these ants put the apostrophes in the correct places below.

An elephants tusks are very hard.

The Suns rays are filtering through the pine forest.

Did you see the animal babies pictures?

Can you hear the flapping of many toucans wings?

These must be the animals footprints!

ADVERB SORTING

Help Hoko the Hippo underline the adverbs and write their type.

I heard the cackling geese just a while ago.

____

How often we hear that tigers must be protected.

____

Everywhere that Mary went, the lamb was sure to go.

____

The lion roared fiercely.

____

The tiger was thirsty. He therefore went to the pond.

____

LET'S COMPARE

Help Ollie the Owl fill in the blanks with the correct degrees of comparison.

The coast redwood is the __________ tree in the world. (sharp)

The big oak is a __________ tree. (large)

The three-wattled bellbird is said to have the __________ bird call. (loud)

Bats, they say, have a __________ sense of hearing than any other animal. (good)

VIXEN'S VOICE

Help Vinnie the Vixen identify and write the correct voice of each sentence.

This is the lion's den.

____

This cave belongs to the bear.

____

The cranes are drinking water.

____

Insects are being eaten by the fish.

____

Why are the bulls fighting?

____

Why is such an argument being raised by the two zebras?

____

HERBIE'S VERBS

Help Herbie the Hyena circle the verbs below. Then, connect them to the right basket.

The town mouse and country mouse were cousins.

The bunny is in his burrow.

Elephants have ivory tusks.

We had a pet turtle.

Rainforests are home to a host of animals and birds.

The kangaroo hopped all round the field.

CATTY CONTRACTIONS

Help Chloe the Cat shorten the bracket words and complete the sentences.

We know __________ been here because of their footprints. (they have)

The dog has seen the cat. __________ soon be chasing it. (it will)

Five little ducks have gone to play. __________ be back this evening. (they will)

__________ been eating grass all day! (I have)

__________ on our way to the forest. (We are)

__________ too big and cannot run very fast. (it is)

TENSES AND TIGERS

Help Tory the Tiger identify the tenses of the underlined words.

These koalas are eating eucalyptus.

____

These pandas have been eating bamboo since an hour!

____

The duck was swimming.

____

The geese had drunk the water an hour ago.

____

The sheep will be going for grazing.

____

The cattle will have eaten fodder.

____

Cuckoos will have been singing tomorrow morning.

____

TENSE TEST

Michelle the Monkey is about to get her grammar tested. Can you help her out?

We will have fewer forests if we are not careful. (rewrite using the future continuous tense)

When we get home, our cat __________ by the fence. (choose - sits, will be sitting)

She has brought some grains. She will be feeding the pigeons. (rewrite using the past perfect tense)

It began to rain when we __________ in an open bus safari. (choose - are, were, will be)

I __________ the fox make a strange sound every night! (choose - heard, hear, will have been hearing)

PERSON PROBLEMS

Help Kerry the Koala match the sentences to the correct leaves.

I must run fast to win the race.

She went to the circus with her friends.

You must not tell lies.

I saw an elephant chewing on some grass.

Did you see the monkey juggling those bananas?

1st person

2nd person

3rd person

DOG TALK

Help the dogs complete their conversation by filling it with prepositions.

Everything has changed so much __________ we last met.

Sigh! Let us share it __________ you and me!

The water __________ the pond seems cold. Brrr!

Let's wait __________ the pond to see if anyone else comes along.

Look!! There's a bone __________ that tree!

behind on under

in beside

We used to share our dog food ________ all our friends.

Would you like a quick dive ________ the pool?

________ the both of us, there seems to be no one else.

Sitting ________ this rock and waiting is not exciting.

Then, let's go, sit ________ it and have a feast.

in   between   with

since

PRONOUN PRACTICE

Help Molly the Monkey fill in the blanks with the correct pronouns from the rocks.

_____ asked _____ not to chase the dog but he didn't listen to me.

That tiger has a white coat. _____ looks beautiful.

Will _____ join us on the safari? _____ are going with some other friends.

We must not take the natural surroundings away from _____.

Will _____ please hold _____ guinea pig for _____? _____ is frightened of strangers.

SENTENCE TEST

Help Rodeo the Rhino score on his sentence test. Rewrite the sentences using the type mentioned in the brackets.

Mary had a little lamb. (Interrogative sentence)

____

Baa, Baa, Black Sheep. Have you any wool?

(Imperative sentence)

____

How sweet is the little yellow hen!

(Declarative sentence)

____

Have mercy on animals.

(Exclamatory sentence)

____

____

PREFIX AND SUFFIX

Help Dino the Dinosaur fill in the blanks using suffixes or prefixes of the words in the brackets.

Dinosaurs are said to be ___________ animals. (historic)

The cat spent ___________ nights looking for the mouse. (sleep)

The rains have made the lake waters ___________. (flow)

Are ducks ___________ sleeping in the water? (comfort)

This ___________ wants to walk through the forest. (sail)

The thunderstorm took place this __________. (noon)

Dogs are said to be man's most __________ friends. (depend)

The elephant got his __________ from the circus soon enough. (free)

The forest meeting had all the animals in __________. (attend)

We must all make an effort to __________ with nature. (connect)

JUNGLE NEWS

Help Crafty the Crow write sentences about the jungle animals using the idioms below.

His bark is worse than his bite

Crocodile tears

Eager beaver

Turn over a new leaf

Let the cat out of the bag

OPPOSITE HUNT

Look at the words on the leaves and find their opposites in the grid below.

wild happy easy sink fast

clean long

full near

old over

wet hot noisy never

<table>
<tr><td>a</td><td>s</td><td>l</td><td>o</td><td>w</td><td>b</td><td>c</td><td>h</td><td>k</td><td>l</td></tr>
<tr><td>l</td><td>a</td><td>l</td><td>w</td><td>a</td><td>y</td><td>s</td><td>m</td><td>i</td><td>n</td></tr>
<tr><td>t</td><td>d</td><td>i</td><td>f</td><td>f</td><td>i</td><td>c</td><td>u</td><td>l</td><td>t</td></tr>
<tr><td>s</td><td>y</td><td>c</td><td>o</td><td>l</td><td>d</td><td>p</td><td>n</td><td>e</td><td>a</td></tr>
<tr><td>p</td><td>t</td><td>s</td><td>h</td><td>o</td><td>r</td><td>t</td><td>d</td><td>f</td><td>m</td></tr>
<tr><td>s</td><td>q</td><td>f</td><td>e</td><td>a</td><td>y</td><td>p</td><td>e</td><td>g</td><td>e</td></tr>
<tr><td>w</td><td>u</td><td>a</td><td>o</td><td>t</td><td>o</td><td>l</td><td>r</td><td>e</td><td>m</td></tr>
<tr><td>d</td><td>i</td><td>r</td><td>t</td><td>y</td><td>u</td><td>h</td><td>p</td><td>v</td><td>p</td></tr>
<tr><td>e</td><td>e</td><td>y</td><td>d</td><td>o</td><td>n</td><td>m</td><td>e</td><td>e</td><td>t</td></tr>
<tr><td>q</td><td>t</td><td>l</td><td>f</td><td>q</td><td>g</td><td>p</td><td>q</td><td>r</td><td>y</td></tr>
</table>

ARTICLE MAZE

Help Barry the Bunny find his way to the article tree. Follow the path with the correct words.

SENTENCE CHECKER

Help Checkers the Cheetah spot the incorrect sentences.

The puppy didn't find the bone neither on nor under the table. ☐

He did not mention neither the lake nor the boating. ☐

Neither are we going to the forest this morning nor to the park. ☐

Either we look for trees in the woods or for flowers. ☐

We must look after our tigers and wild life otherwise neither will they survive or other animals. ☐

The cat will either purr or meow! ☐

SWIRLING SIMILES

Help Slither the Snake complete the similes and form sentences using them.

As busy as a ____________________

____

As free as a ____________________

____

As hairy as a ____________________

____

As hungry as a ____________________

____

As gentle as a ____________________

____

MOMO'S METAPHORS

Help Momo the Monkey identify the metaphors in the following sentences.

How can you listen to that snake?

He does all the donkey work.

The new boy in our class is a sheep.

He was a lion in the meeting.

We flocked to see the new movie.

PICTURE STORY

Look at the pictures given below. Then, write a story based on them on the next page.

1

2

3

4

5

6

PHRASE ALERT

Help Jojo the Jungle Police Officer spot and circle the phrases in the following sentences.

A pretty pink flamingo stood by the lake.

A lot of kids are really keen on a forest trail.

I wanted to capture the moments in pictures as fast as possible.

The cat is sleeping under the table.

DEAR LION

The King of the Jungle is rude to all his subjects. Write a letter to him, telling him to be kinder to them.

To, ____________________

____

From, ____________________

____

POETRY TIME

Read the poem and answer the questions that follow.

Doris the dragon
Didn't know what to eat,
For she had a problem;
She didn't like meat.

She didn't like vegetables,
Which wasn't so good.
And her mother didn't know
What to give her as food.

Then one day papa dragon
Went out for lunch.
And brought little Doris
Some sugarcane to munch.

Fussy little Doris
Gobbled the whole cane.
"This is what I want to eat
Again and again."

Doris's poor mother
Heaved a sigh of relief.
Her daughter was finally eating
Which put an end to her grief!

Who was Doris?

____

What did she not eat?

____

What did her father bring for her?

____

Who heaved a sigh of relief?

____

ANIMAL ESSAYS

Choose any animal you like and write an essay about it. You could use the points given below.

habitat eating habits features caring uniqueness

ANSWERS

Page 2

Cows give **milk**. (Identify the nouns)

They eat grass. (Identify the pronoun)

These cows are **white** in colour. (Identify the adjective)

They are **walking** in the meadows. (Identify the verb)

The cows have **very** cute bells around their necks. (Identify the adverb)

That cow is sitting **under** a tree. (Identify the preposition)

This cow is white **and** that one is brown. (Identify the conjunction)

Oh! Their milk is so sweet! (Identify the interjection)

Page 3

An **elephant's** tusks are very hard.

The **Sun's** rays are filtering through the pine forest.

Did you see the animal **babies'** pictures?

Can you hear the flapping of many **toucan's** wings?

These must be the **animals'** footprints!

Page 4

I heard the cackling geese just a while ago.
Adverb of time

How often we hear that tigers must be protected.
Adverb of time

Everywhere that Mary went, the lamb was sure to go.
Adverb of place

The lion roared fiercely.
Adverb of manner

The tiger was thirsty. He therefore went to the pond.
Adverb of reason

Page 5

The coast redwood is the **sharpest** tree in the world. (sharp)

The big oak is a **large** tree. (large)

The three-wattled bellbird is said to have the **loudest** bird call. (loud)

Bats, they say, have a **better** sense of hearing than any other animal. (good)

Page 6

This is the lion's den.
Active voice

This cave belongs to the bear.
Active voice

The cranes are drinking water.
Active voice

Insects are being eaten by the fish.
Passive voice

Why are the bulls fighting?
Active voice

Why is such an argument being raised by the two zebras?
Passive voice

Page7

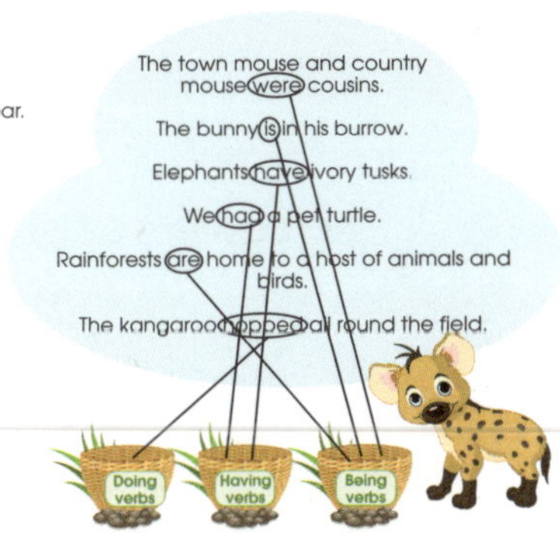

Page 8

We know **they've** been here because of their footprints. (they have)

The dog has seen the cat. **It'll** soon be chasing it. (It will)

Five little ducks have gone to play. **They'll** be back this evening. (they will)

I've been eating grass all day! (I have)

We're on our way to the forest. (We are)

It's too big and cannot run very fast. (It is)

Page 9

These koalas are eating eucalyptus.
Present continuous tense

These pandas have been eating bamboo since an hour!
Present perfect continuous tense

The duck was swimming.
Past continuous tense

The geese had drunk the water an hour ago.
Past perfect tense

The sheep will be going for grazing.
Future continuous tense

The cattle will have eaten fodder.
Future perfect tense

Cuckoos will have been singing tomorrow morning.
Future perfect continuous tense

Page 10

We will have fewer forests if we are not careful. (rewrite using the future continuous tense)
We will be having fewer forests if we are not careful.

When we get home, our cat **will be sitting** by the fence. (choose - sits, will be sitting)

She has brought some grains. She will be feeding the pigeons. (rewrite using the Past perfect tense)
She had brought some grains. She had fed the pigeons.

It began to rain when we **were** in an open bus safari. (choose - are, were, will be)

I **hear** the fox make a strange sound every night! (choose - heard, hear, will have been hearing)

Page 11

Page 12

Everything has changed so much **since** we last met.

Sigh! Let us share it **between** you and me!

The water **in** the pond seems cold. Brrr!

Let's wait **beside** the pond to see if anyone else comes along.

Look!! There's a bone **behind** that tree!

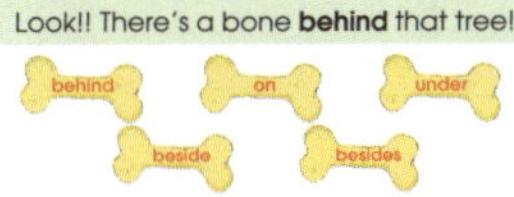

Page 13

We used to share our dog food **with** all our friends.

Would you like a quick dive **in** the pool?

Between the both of us, there seems to be no one else.

Sitting **on** this rock and waiting is not exciting.

Then, let's go, sit **under** it and have a feast.

Page 14

I asked **him** not to chase the dog but he didn't listen to me.

The tiger has a white coat. **It** looks beautiful.

Will **you** join us on the safari? **We** are going with some other friends.

We must not take the natural surroundings away from **them**.

Will **you** please hold **my** guinea pig for **me**? **It** frightened of strangers.

Page 15

Mary had a little lamb. (Interrogative sentence)
Did Mary have a little lamb?

Baa, Baa, Black Sheep. Have you any wool? (Imperative sentence)
Baa, Baa, Black Sheep. Give me some wool.

How sweet is the little yellow hen! (Declarative sentence)
The little yellow hen is very sweet.

Have mercy on animals. (Exclamatory sentence)
Please! Have mercy on animals!

Page 16

Dinosaurs are said to be **prehistoric** animals. (historic)

The cat spent **sleepless** night looking for the mouse. (sleep)

The rains have made the lake waters **overflow**. (flow)

Are ducks **comfortable** sleeping in the water? (comfort)

This **sailor** wants to walk through the forest. (sail)

Page 17

The thunderstorm took place this **afternoon**. (noon)

Dogs are said to be man's most **dependable** friends. (depend)

The elephant got his **freedom** for the circus soon enough. (free)

The forest meeting had all the animals in **attendance**. (attend)

We must all make an effort to **reconnect** with nature. (connect)

ANSWERS

Page 19

wild, happy, easy, sink, fast, clean, long, full, near, old, over, wet, hot, noisy, never

a	s	l	o	w	b	c	h	k	l
l	a	l	w	a	y	s	m	i	n
t	d	i	f	f	i	c	u	l	t
s	y	c	o	l	d	p	n	e	a
p	t	s	h	o	r	t	d	f	m
s	q	f	e	a	y	p	e	g	e
w	u	a	o	t	o	l	r	e	m
d	i	r	t	y	u	h	p	v	p
e	e	y	d	o	n	m	e	e	t
q	t	l	f	q	g	p	q	r	y

Page 20

Page 21

The puppy didn't find the bone neither on nor under the table. ✗

He did not mention neither the lake nor the boating. ✗

Neither are we going to the forest this morning nor to the park. ✓

Either we look for trees in the woods or for flowers. ✓

We must look after our tigers and wild life otherwise neither will they survive or other animals. ✗

The cat will either purr or meow! ✓

Page 22

As busy as a **bee**

As free as a **bird**

As hairy as a **bear**

As hungry as a **horse**

As gentle as a **sheep**

Page 23

How can you listen to that **snake**?

He does all the **donkey** work.

The new boy in our class is a **sheep**.

He was **a lion** in the meeting.

We **flocked** to see the new movie.

Page 26

A pretty pink flamingo **stood by the lake**.

A lot of kids are really keen **on a forest trail**.

I wanted to capture the moments in pictures **as fast as possible**.

The cat is sleeping **under the table**.

Page 29

Who was Doris?
Doris was a dragon.

What did she not eat?
She didn't eat meat and vegetables.

What did her father bring for her?
Her father brought sugarcane for her.

Who heaved a sigh of relief?
Dori's mother heaved a sigh of relief.

Hammer your Grammar

Workbook Grade 4

An imprint of Om Books International

POETRY TIME

Read the poem, circle the nouns and write their type.

Polly the parrot,

____

Was a pirate at sea.

____

And she was happier,

____

Than any pirate could be.

____

She saw such crazy sights,

____

Like dolphins wearing rings,

____

And whales who liked to gobble,

____

Mouldy green things.

____

She met crazy dogs,

Who lived on rows of trees.

And funny little monkeys,

With guitars on their knees.

Then one day she met a parrot,

Who was both handsome and jolly.

And that was the last we saw,

Of our beloved pirate Polly.

JUNGLE SCRAMBLE

Fill in the letters to complete the crossword. Unscramble the letters on the leaves to get your clues.

rtoligaal | ndaap | rlisuqre | cuihenarr

tra | oanrc | kle | ele

doaerlp | aleeg | tetro | ldtpeao

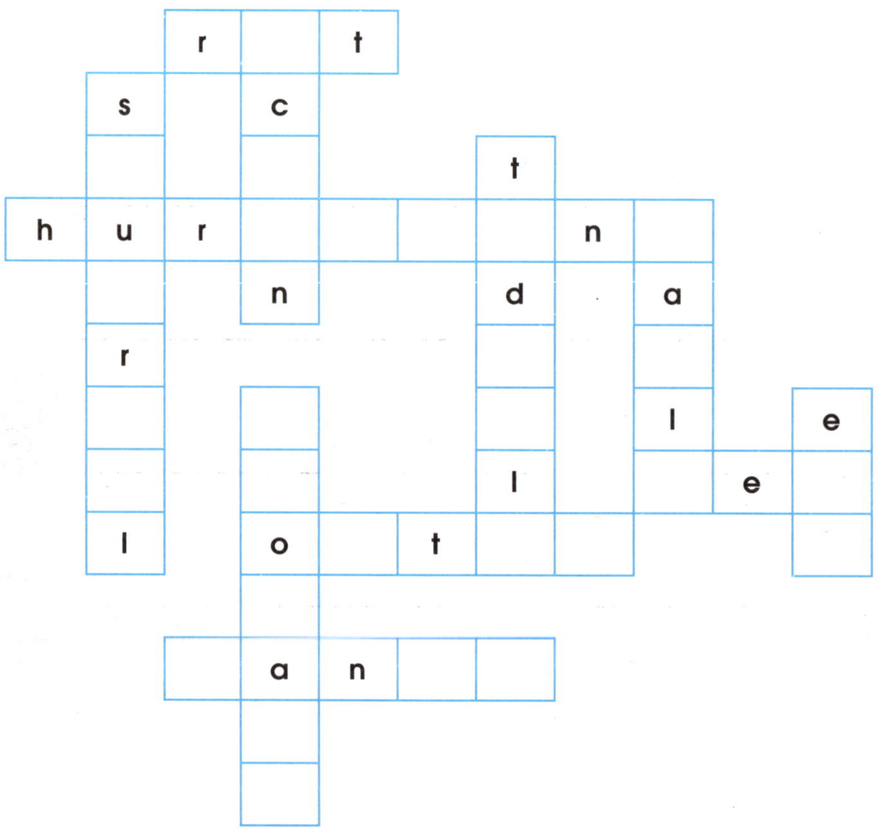

THE PATH TO PRONOUNS

Circle the right word in the bracket to complete the path correctly.

(Us, We) plucked fresh herbs from the woods.

Will you let (us, we) help you cook?

(You, Your, Yours, You're) the best friend I've ever had.

(You, Your, Yours, You're) was the best birthday party.

(You, Your, Yours, You're) coat is so soft!

(You, Your, Yours, You're) are very special!

PUNCTUATION JUNCTION

Help the animals place the correct punctuation and reach the forest junction.

the teacher says look children theres a rainbow in the sky the poet william wordsworth said my heart leaps up when I behold a rainbow in the sky the colours of the rainbow are violet indigo blue green yellow orange and red

the children all shout in delight yes they want to catch a rainbow which of course they cant have you ever tried to catch a rainbow

as the children try to walk into the forest their teacher exclaims look what a pretty sight this is there are baby birds in that nest

back at school the children were asked would you like to go again write a short story about your school trip

PUZZLING!

Danny the Dinosaur wants to know if the underlined words are adjectives or adverbs. Write the correct answer on the blanks.

Look at the bubbly monkey jumping up and down the tree.

____

Oh! See the graceful galloping of the enchanting mare.

____

The big redwood trees are remarkably tall!

____

The black koel sings beautifully.

____

White pandas look cute.

____

That small puppy was born yesterday.

____

____

COMPARISON CLASS

Help Kelly the Kangaroo prepare for her comparison class by filling the chart below.

Positive	Comparative	Superlative
beautiful		
	farther / further	
		oldest / eldest
lazy		
large		
	larger	
		sweetest
	more intelligent	
thin		
	younger	

TENSE TALES

Help Rocky the Rabbit fill in the blanks using the correct tense of the words in brackets.

We must ____________ awareness about our ecology. (to build)

Jungle Book will make you ____________ in love with animals. (to fall)

He ____________ that he would never ill treat the dog again. (to say)

Have you ____________ the lamp by the sleeping cubs? (to see)

The ducks ____________ in the lake last evening. (to swim)

She ____________ the carrots for her pet rabbits so she could give them later. (to save)

We stopped them from ____________ the trees. (to cut)

Have you ____________ past the woods in the morning? It is a beautiful feeling. (to walk)

VERB WORM

Help Whizzy the Worm fill in the blanks with the correct verb.

- Jack and Jill _________ environmentalists. (is / are)
- Either Jack or Jill _________ an environmentalist. (is / are)
- Black wattle, candle nut and red tulip nut _________ in rainforests. (grow / grows)
- My dog and cat _________ together. (play / plays)
- Her pets and mine _________ come for a walk. (has / have)
- Neither Jack nor Jill _________ an environmentalist. (is / are)
- In forests, big animals and small ones _________ in unity. (live / lives)

- The big and the small __________ forward in times of need. (come / comes)
- Neither she nor her cubs __________ come to the clearing. (has / have)
- Either a ball or a few rings __________ used to train animals in a circus. (is / are)
- There __________ a hundred things that animals do in a day. (is / are)
- The majority __________ in favour of the nature walk. (is / are)
- She __________ the birds every day. (feed / feeds)

are have
plays feeds
lives
comes

CATTY CLAUSE

Terry the Tiger wants to learn about clauses. Can you underline them in the following sentences? A clause is a part of a sentence with a subject and a predicate of its own.

If you do not take care, you will have no water.

When the sun sets, birds go to sleep.

Here is the pet that you wanted.

It was the storm that knocked some trees down.

I thought that today would be a sunny day.

Can you see the birds by the lake?

SENTENCE SORTING

Help Slither the Snake categorise these sentences by ticking the correct boxes.

The big brown bear ran after the pot of honey.

☐ Simple ☐ Complex ☐ Compound

Many people watched the movie Jungle Book and liked it.

☐ Simple ☐ Complex ☐ Compound

My dog and cat slept after they drank milk.

☐ Simple ☐ Complex ☐ Compound

Before we begin our journey, let's read about the trip.

☐ Simple ☐ Complex ☐ Compound

After dark, the owls will hoot.

☐ Simple ☐ Complex ☐ Compound

Although she was unwell, she attended class.

☐ Simple ☐ Complex ☐ Compound

THE GRASSHOPPER AND THE ANT

Fill in their conversation with the right question words.

who where why what whom how when which whose

Grasshopper

Ant

__________ are you doing?

__________ thinks about winter now?

__________ is winter? Far away!

__________ is the right thing to do?

Gathering food for the winter. __________ don′t you do the same?

I do. When winter comes __________ will you go?

__________ will you ask for food then?

__________ house will you knock at when winter arrives?

VERB ALERT

Jinx the Jackal stole verbs from the sentences. Can you return them to the correct places?

We __________ to respect animals and plants.

__________ I use your pictures for my project?

We __________ take the bus for our field trip tomorrow, although it is not certain.

The forest officer __________ be taking down our names.

Please, __________ you sit down and explain the life-cycle of a butterfly?

I __________ show you the way to the forest river.

JUNGLE JUMBLE

The animals have a test to complete! Help them finish it.

Match and complete.

Let's write a ____________ on animal conservation.

Let's ____________ after lunch.

The mosquito ____________ him.

May I have a ____________ of sugar in my coffee?

bit
bit
play
play

Fill in the blanks with homographs.

wound, present

Are all the students ____________ today?

The teacher will ____________ the marks now.

The rope was ____________ around the snake.

He received a small ____________ while playing.

Choose the right option.

We will not ____________ water.
(waste / waist)

May I go for the play ____________?
(too / to)

The horse ____________ away without its master.
(rode / road)

The ____________ spoke to the parents.
(principle / principal)

Fill in the blanks.

The ____________ ran away with the honey.
(bear / bare)

____________ of them know their way to the lake. (nun / none)

The dolphin lives in the deep blue ____________.
(sea / see)

OPPOSITES ATTRACT

An oxymoron is a phrase that uses two words with opposite meanings. Match the lion's words to the tiger's and make some oxymorons.

Lion	Tiger
all	sweat
detailed	alone
cold	summary
half	fool
wise	crowd
small	full

DIRECTLY INDIRECT

Joky the Jackal loves changing conversations around. Can you help him rewrite these sentences using indirect speech?

The fox said, "I want those grapes!"

The shepherd thought, "I am bored!"

The grasshopper said to the ant, "Why are you working so hard?"

The mouse asked the lion, "Was I not right?"

PEPPERING PREPOSITIONS

Help Dingo the Dog fill in the blanks with prepositions.

My dog jumped ________ of the window and ________ my car.

Walk ________ the corridor and you will find the sleeping kitten.

The circus elephant climbed ________ the stairs.

The rabbit jumped ________ the fence and ran ________ the garden.

The bull ran ________ the spectators.

The cub saw place ________ two trees and rested there.

ANIMAL ANALOGIES

Complete the analogies for the animals below.

A cow is to milk as a ____________ is to eggs.

Fleet is to ships as ____________ is to elephants.

Bird is to feather as ____________ is to wool.

Bird is to fly as fish is to ____________.

Duck is to duckling as horse is to ____________.

PATRICK'S PROVERB STORE

Patrick the Parrot sells proverbs in the jungle. Help him sort them out by choosing the correct meaning for each one.

Bull in a China shop.

- There's a shop in China with a bull in it. ☐
- There are shops in China which have bulls. ☐
- To be very clumsy. ☐

Rats abandoning a sinking ship.

- When a ship sinks, there are rats on it. ☐
- Rats live on ships. ☐
- People who are not loyal. ☐

Smell a rat.

- To be suspicious of something or get the feeling that something is wrong. ☐
- Find the smell of a rat. ☐
- See a rat and try to find it. ☐

Don't cut down the tree that gives you shade.

Trees give shade so we must not cut them down. ☐

Never cut a tree. ☐

Never harm or hurt something or someone that does good to you. ☐

If you call one wolf, you invite the pack.

One bad habit leads to another. ☐

One wolf calls another. ☐

A group of wolves is called a pack. ☐

Lock the stable door after the horse has run.

After the horse runs, lock the stable door. ☐

To prevent something that has already happened from happening. ☐

Don't lock stable doors, or the horses will run. ☐

SIMILE SURPRISE

Match the similes to the correct animals.

As fresh as a

As cunning as a

As innocent as a

As happy as a

As wise as an

As hungry as a

A stubborn as a

owl

bear

lark

lamb

fox

mule

daisy

PART PATHS

Read the sentences and identify the parts of speech for the underlined words.

Since this afternoon, the dog has been barking.

____

Since there's nothing else to do, let's go for a walk.

____

I have not seen my cat ever since.

____

Well, what an unusual bird!

____

Is the tiger well now?

____

The bird fell in the well.

____

ONCE UPON A TALE

Create a jungle story based on Oliver the Owl's outline.

Animals in a jungle – constant fights – no one likes each other – jungle lake goes dry – no water – animals look for a solution – some animals team up and bring water from a nearby jungle – everyone stops fighting.

PEPPER'S POETRY

Help Pepper the Penguin write a poem about himself. Use the rhyming words from the ice cubes.

POEM PROBLEMS

Let's read Jinny's poem and answer the questions that follow.

Jinny the giraffe,
was tall and thin.
And what she loved,
was to always win.

She would win at basketball,
and star gazing too.
She would win a free ice cream,
on a picnic to the zoo.

She would win at playing catch,
or a clever game of chess.
And at costume parties,
she would win for the best dress.

But Jinny's friends didn't hate her.
She was actually quite nice.
For every time she won,
she shared her lovely prize.

Who was Jinny?

____

____

What was she good at?

____

____

Did the other animals hate her for being good?

____

____

What did she do with her prizes?

____

____

What do you learn from Jinny?

____

____

A JUNGLE'S TALE

If you were a jungle, what would you be like? Write an essay about yourself as a jungle.

ANSWERS

Page 2

Polly the parrot.
Proper noun Common noun

Was a pirate at sea.
Common noun

And she was happier,

Than any pirate could be.
Common noun

She saw such crazy sights.
Common noun

Like dolphins wearing rings.
Common noun

And whales who liked to gobble,
Common noun

Mouldy green things.
Common noun

Page 3

She met crazy dogs,
Common noun

Who lived on rows of trees.
Collective noun Common noun

And funny little monkeys,
Common noun

With guitars on their knees.
Common noun

Then one day she met a parrot.
Common noun

Who was both handsome and jolly

And that was the last we saw,

Of our beloved pirate Polly.
Common noun Proper noun

Page 4

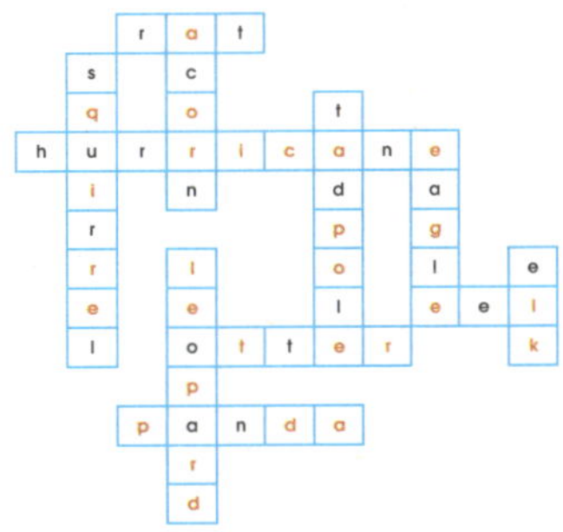

Page 5

(Us, **We**) plucked fresh herbs from the woods.

Will you let (**us**, we) help you cook?

(You, Your, Yours, **You're**) the best friend I've ever had.

(You, Your, **Yours**, You're) was the best birthday party.

(You, **Your**, Yours, You're) coat is so soft!

(**You**, Your, Yours, You're) are very special!

Page 6

The teacher says, "Look children, there's a rainbow in the sky!" The poet William Wordsworth said, "My heart leaps up when I behold a rainbow in the sky." The colours of the rainbow are violet, indigo, blue, green, yellow, orange and red.

The children all shout in delight, "Yes!" They want to catch a rainbow, which, of course, they can't. Have you ever tried to catch a rainbow?

As the children try to walk into the forest, their teacher exclaims, "Look! What a pretty sight this is! There are baby birds in that nest."

Back at school, the children were asked, "Would you like to go again? Write a short story about your school trip."

Page 7

Look at the bubbly monkey jumping up and down the tree.
1. bubbly - adjective, 2. up and down - adverb

Oh! See the graceful galloping of the enchanting mare.
1. graceful - adverb, 2. enchanting - adjective

The big redwood trees are remarkably tall!
1. big - adjective, 2. remarkably - adverb

The black koel sings beautifully.
1. black - adjective, 2. beautifully - adverb

White pandas look cute.
1. White - adjective, 2. cute - adjective

That small puppy was born yesterday.
1. small - adjective, 2. yesterday - adverb

Page 8

Positive	Comparative	Superlative
beautiful	**more beautiful**	**most beautiful**
far	farther / further	**farthest**
old	**older / elder**	oldest / eldest
lazy	**lazier**	**laziest**
large	larger	**largest**
sweet	**sweeter**	sweetest
intelligent	more intelligent	**most intelligent**
thin	**thinner**	**thinnest**
young	younger	**youngest**

Page 9

We must **build** awareness about our ecology.

Jungle Book will make you **fall** in love with animals.

He **said** that he would never ill treat the dog again.

Have you **seen** the lamp by the sleeping cubs?

The ducks **swam** in the lake last evening.

She **saved** the carrots for her pet rabbits so she could give them later.

We stopped them from **cutting** the trees.

Have you **walked** past the woods in the morning? It is a beautiful feeling.

Page 10

Jack and Jill **are** environmentalists. (is / are)

Either Jack or Jill **is** an environmentalist. (is / are)

Black Wattle, Candle Nut and Red Tulip Nut **grow** in Rainforests. (grow / grows)

My dog and cat **play** together. (play / plays)

Her pets and mine **have** come for a walk. (has / have)

Neither Jack nor Jill **is** an environmentalist. (is / are)

In forests, big animals and small ones **live** in unity. (live / lives)

Page 11

The big and the small **come** forward in times of need. (come / comes)

Neither she nor her cubs **have** come to the clearing. (has / have)

Either a ball or a few rings **are** used to train animals in a circus. (is / are)

There **are** a hundred things that animals do in a day. (is / are)

The majority **is** in favour of the nature walk. (is / are)

She **feeds** the birds every day. (feed / feeds)

Page 12

If you do not take care, you will have no water.

When the sun sets, birds go to sleep.

Here is the pet **that you wanted**.

It was the storm **that knocked some trees down**.

I thought **that today would be a sunny day**.

Can you see the birds **by the lake**?

Page 13

The big brown bear ran after the pot of honey.
☑ Simple ☐ Complex ☐ Compound

Many people watched the movie Jungle Book and liked it.
☐ Simple ☐ Complex ☑ Compound

My dog and cat slept after they drank milk.
☐ Simple ☐ Complex ☑ Compound

Before we begin our journey, let's read about the trip.
☐ Simple ☑ Complex ☐ Compound

After dark, the owls will hoot.
☐ Simple ☑ Complex ☐ Compound

Although she was unwell, she attended class.
☐ Simple ☑ Complex ☐ Compound

Page 14

Grasshopper	Ant
What are you doing?	Gathering food for the winter. **Why** don't you do the same?
Who thinks of winter now?	I do. When winter comes **Where** will you go?
When is winter? Far away!	**How** will you ask for food then?
What is the right thing to do?	**Which** house will you knock at when winter arrives?

Page 15

We **ought** to respect animals and plants.

May I use your pictures for my project?

We **might** take the bus for our field trip tomorrow, although it is not certain.

The forest officer **will** be taking down our names.

Please, **would** you sit down and explain the life-cycle of the butterfly?

I **shall** show you the way to the forest river.

Page 16

Match and complete.

Let's write a ________ on animal conservation. — play
Let's ________ after lunch. — play
The mosquito ________ him — bit
May I have a ________ of sugar in my coffee? — bit

Fill in the blanks with homographs.

words – wound, present

Are all the students **present** today?

The teacher will **present** the marks now.

The rope was **wound** around the snake.

He received a small **wound** while playing.

Page 17

Choose the right option.

We will not **waste** water. (waste / waist)

May I go for the play **too**? (too / to)

The horse **rode** away without its master. (rode / road)

The **principal** spoke to the parents. (principle / principal)

Fill in the blanks.

The **bear** ran away with the honey. (bear / bare)

None of them know their way to the lake. (nun / none)

The dolphin lives in the deep blue **sea**. (sea / see)

ANSWERS

Page 18

Page 19

The fox said, "I want those grapes!"
The fox said that he wanted those grapes.

The shepherd thought, "I am bored!"
The shepherd thought that he was bored.

The grasshopper said to the ant, "Why are you working so hard?"
The grasshopper asked the ant why he was working so hard.

The mouse asked the lion, "Was I not right?"
The mouse asked the lion if he was not right.

Page 20

My dog jumped **out** of the window and **into** my car.

Walk **along** the corridor and you will find the sleeping kitten.

The circus elephant climbed **up** the stairs.

The rabbit jumped **over** the fence and ran **into** the garden.

The bull ran **towards** the spectators.

The cub saw place **between** two trees and rested there.

Page 21

A cow is to milk as a **hen** is to eggs.

Fleet is to ships as **herd** is to elephants.

Bird is to feather as **sheep** is to wool.

Bird is to fly as fish is to **swim**.

Duck is to duckling as horse is to **foal**.

Page 22

Bull in a China shop.
- There's a shop in China with a bull in it. ☐
- There are shops in China which have bulls. ☐
- To be very clumsy ☑

Rats abandoning a sinking ship.
- When a ship sinks, there are rats on it. ☐
- Rats live on ships. ☐
- People who are not loyal. ☑

Smell a rat.
- To be suspicious of something or get the feeling that something is wrong ☑
- Find the smell of a rat. ☐
- See a rat and try to find it. ☐

Page 23

Don't cut down the tree that gives you shade.
- Trees give shade so we must not cut them down. ☐
- Never cut a tree. ☐
- Never harm or hurt something or someone that does good to you. ☑

If you call one wolf, you invite the pack.
- One bad habit leads to another. ☑
- One wolf calls another. ☐
- A group of wolves is called a pack. ☐

Lock the stable door after the horse has run.
- After the horse runs, lock the stable door. ☐
- To prevent something that has already happened from happening. ☑
- Don't lock stable doors, or the horses will run. ☐

Page 24

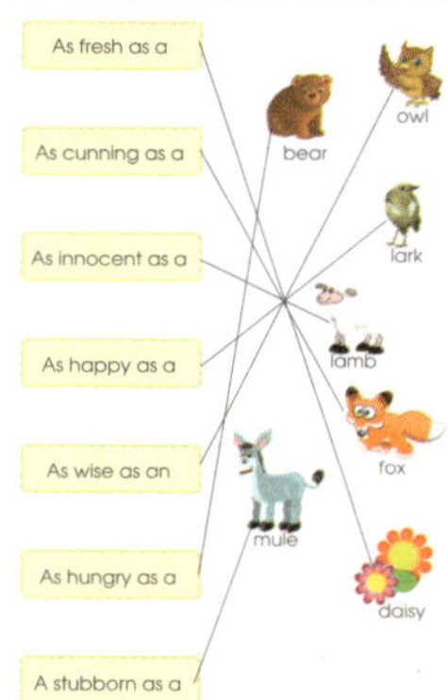

Page 25

Since this afternoon the dog has been barking.
Preposition

Since there's nothing else to do, let's go for a walk.
Preposition

I have not seen my cat ever since.
Adverb

Well, what an unusual bird!
interjection

Is the tiger well now?
Adjective

The bird fell in the well.
Noun

Page 29

Who was Jinny?
She was a giraffe.

What was she good at?
She was good at winning.

Did the other animals hate her for being good?
No, they did not.

What did she do with her prizes?
She share her prizes.

What do you learn from Jinny?
We must always share.